This book belongs to:

_____

# The Troll-tastic GUIDE to

## DreamWorks

# Trolls

centum

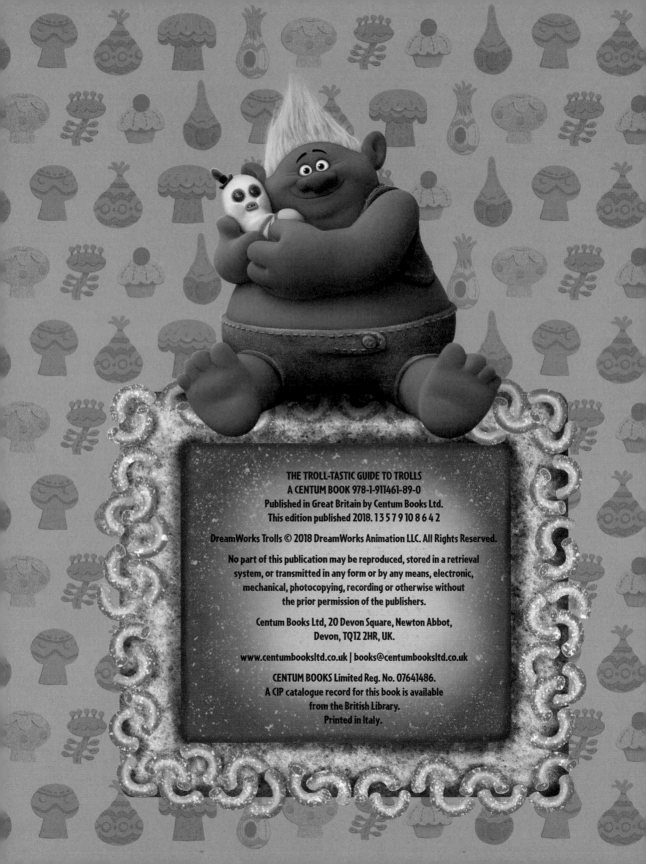

THE TROLL-TASTIC GUIDE TO TROLLS
A CENTUM BOOK 978-1-911461-89-0
Published in Great Britain by Centum Books Ltd.
This edition published 2018. 13 5 7 9 10 8 6 4 2

Centum Books Ltd, 20 Devon Square, Newton Abbot,
Devon, TQ12 2HR, UK.

www.centumbooksltd.co.uk | books@centumbooksltd.co.uk

CENTUM BOOKS Limited Reg. No. 07641486.
A CIP catalogue record for this book is available
from the British Library.
Printed in Italy.

# CONTENTS

# HISTORY

Before you enter the world of the Trolls here's a Troll-sized history lesson...

Once upon a time the unhappy Bergens discovered the super-happy and super-tasty Trolls. They kept them captive to eat on Trollstice...

...But the Trolls escaped before the Bergen's chef could serve them up for Prince Gristle's first Trollstice feast.

**'NO TROLL LEFT BEHIND!'**

Twenty years pass, and the day of Poppy's coronation finally arrives. The Trolls celebrate with an extra loud party.

The Bergen ex-Royal Chef overhears the party. Finally, she can get her revenge! She captures some of the Trolls.

Poppy decides to rescue her friends. When her friend Branch refuses to help, she sets out alone.

Branch has a change of mind and catches up to Poppy just in time to save her from a terrible fate. Optimistic Poppy sings all the way to Bergen Town.

9

'OH MY GAH!'

The Trolls befriend Bridget, a shy Bergen scullery maid, and discover she's in love with King Gristle!

The Trolls offer to help Bridget catch the eye of the King. Lady Glittersparkles is born!

To save himself, a Troll called Creek betrays the Trolls and helps Chef capture the rest of Troll Village. Poppy loses hope and her colour fades away.

Branch sings to Poppy, restoring her positivity and her colours. Branch's true colours return too!

Bridget frees the Trolls. Poppy worries what will happen to her new Bergen friend and turns back to help her.

'NOBODY LEFT BEHIND!'

'HOORAY!'

The Bergens learn that happiness is found within, not from eating Trolls. Poppy is handed the Torch of Freedom and crowned queen.

11

# World of TROLLS

'I love everything about Troll Village. It's completely magical, all neon-bright and sinkably soft, and we're tucked away cosy and safe in a sun-splashed clearing deep in the woods. The whole place is so deliciously fuzzy it practically demands petting, from the cheerful, fluffy flowers on the fuzzy carpet of ground to our plush, multicoloured felt pods that dangle from tree branches on super-strong strands of Troll hair. Every last inch of Troll Village induces happiness.'

-HARPER

# TROLL VILLAGE

You can't possibly get to know the Trolls without stopping for a visit in Troll Village! The problem is that there are so many wonderful things to see and do that you couldn't possibly fit it all in one day. So to help you out we've put together our favourite things to see and do.

Before we begin, take a stroll through the heart of Troll Village. All around you are fuzzy and fluffy plants just waiting to be petted! Look up. Can you see all the multicoloured pods hanging in the trees? Those Troll pods are homes, art studios, hair salons, almost anything you can imagine! And the string holding up these wondrous felt creations? Troll hair of course! So hop on your nearest Caterbus and take a ride deeper into Troll Village.

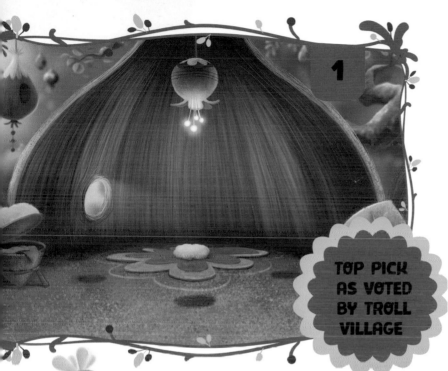

**TOP PICK AS VOTED BY TROLL VILLAGE**

## 1. POPPY'S POD

Where better to start a tour of Troll Village than at the home of the Troll queen herself? Poppy's pod is party central, and Trolls are always receiving handmade invitations to her home.

## 2. HARPER'S ART PARTY POD

This colourful pod is a creative mecca where all Trolls are welcome to express their true colours. If you're lucky you might even have your artwork displayed in Harper's pop-up gallery. Be careful though! Trolls use their hair as paintbrushes so paint is always flying across the room. It might not just be your canvas that receives some colour!

15

## 3. TROLL VILLAGE CUPCAKERY

The sugar-filled cupcakery is a popular destination in Troll Village. The secret ingredient in the magical recipes? The happy tears of Trolls!

## 4. KARMA'S GROOVY GARDEN

Safe and protected within her greenhouse, Karma uses her garden to grow a variety of fruits and vegetables (in case a Troll wants a break from cupcakes). Not only is it filled to the brim with bursts of colour, but the food from Karma's garden is always extra tasty thanks to Troll Village's enchanted soil.

## 5. A, B, SING!

Here is where all the young Trolls come to learn how to sing and dance. This welcoming pod is the perfect environment for learning to let your true colours shine!

## 6. GUY DIAMOND'S GLITTERISH GROOVES

This is Guy Diamond's favourite place to be, besides the Glitter District of course! Fortunately, this pod has a permanent disco ball to keep the dancers sparkling when this glittery Troll isn't around.

## 6. MADDY'S HAIR IN THE AIR SALON

Run by Maddy, the local hair salon guarantees a Troll-do arranged in the most magical of shapes and styles. It's the perfect place to get ready for Poppy's next party.

7

## 6. BRANCH'S SURVIVAL BUNKER

We've saved the most unusual place for last! Unlike any other Troll in Troll Village, Branch built himself a sturdy bunker to live in, complete with periscope and booby traps. No felt pods for this Troll! This bunker is a must-see location in Troll Village... that is if you can find its hidden entrance!

8

GO AWAY

17

# TROLL LIFESTYLE

Now that you've been for a ride around the village, it's time to really experience the Troll way of life. It's not all cupcakes and rainbows... there is also hugging and singing and dancing, and it all comes with a healthy helping of glitter!

## HUG TIME

Drop everything! It's Hug Time! Trolls love to hug. In fact, they love it so much that it was made into an hourly event! Every hour, on the hour, a flower blossoms on every Troll's magical Hug Time watch. At that moment they grab those nearest them and pull them into an epic group hug. The more Trolls the better! After all, who couldn't use a hug?

## HAIR

A Troll's hair does so much more than make a personality statement. It's also a crucial part of a Troll's day-to-day lifestyle. Troll hair is super-strong and the Trolls can stretch and shape their hair instantly into any form you can imagine! Trolls are regularly seen swinging or zip-lining through the trees by their hair, or snoozing in a temporary Troll hair hammock. When it comes to Troll hair, the possibilities are endless!

## MUSIC

The only things Trolls love more than hugging are singing and dancing. With its sweet acoustics Troll Village is constantly pulsing with music, and it's not unusual for a single song to begin an impromptu all-day dance party! Music is a very important element of the Troll lifestyle, and opportunities to express themselves in song and dance are never passed up. Even the local critters are known to join in to create some wicked harmonies. As Poppy says: 'with a song in your heart, anything is possible!'

19

## CRAFTING

Satin and Chenille, the fashion twins, are known for their creations. But they're not the only ones who enjoy creating new things. All Trolls love to express themselves with a little (or a lot) of crafting. Troll Village is full of fun colours and textures the Trolls can use when working on their artworks, outfits, scrapbooks... you name it! Poppy's headband and dress are made of felt and her scrapbook is full of the same fuzzy material (but with a coat of glitter for good measure).

## CRITTERS

Troll Village is not only filled with the most loving and optimistic creatures that ever existed, but is also home to a wide array of friendly and huggable critters. From Biggie's pet worm, Mr Dinkles, to the Caterbuses, the critters of Troll Village are just as much a part of the Trolls' lives as Hug Time! They create tasty treats, form sweet harmonies, help Trolls zoom around the village and some even assist DJ Suki in creating her sick beats!

# PLAN YOUR TRIP!

With so much to see and do in Troll Village we've made a handy itinerary to help you see all the hot spots!

## START

**9.00AM**
HUG TIME!

**9.05AM**
Start the day with some singing and dancing. Go and visit the young Trolls at the school house.

**10.00AM**
HUG TIME!

**10.05AM**
It's snack time! Make your way over to the cupcakery for some sweet treats.

**11.00AM**
HUG TIME!

**11.05AM**
Harper can't wait to welcome you to her art studio! She might even put your work on display in the Follow Your Art Gallery!

**12.00PM**
HUG TIME!

**12.05PM**
Head on over to Karma's garden for a tasty (and rainbow-coloured) lunch!

**1.00PM**
HUG TIME!

**1.03PM**
Pop into the dance studio and practise your favourite dance moves with Guy Diamond. Hope you don't mind being covered in glitter!

**2.00PM**
HUG TIME!

**2.05PM**
After all that dancing it must be time for some more cupcakes. Back to the cupcakery!

**3.00PM**
HUG TIME!

**3.05PM**
Time for a game of seek. See if you can find the entrance to Branch's bunker.

**4.00PM**
HUG TIME!

**4.05PM**
Head over to the local hair salon to remove the paint from your hair and get yourself ready for tonight's party!

**5.00PM**
HUG TIME!

**5.05PM**
Party at Poppy's pod!

21

# HA HA!

**Why did the Troll take a pencil to bed?**

To draw the curtains.

**What has two legs but can't walk?**

Creek's pants.

**What sparkles and goes up and down and up and down?**

Guy Diamond on a trampoline.

**Why did the Troll teacher wear sunglasses?**

Because her students were so bright.

24

# What is a *TROLL?*

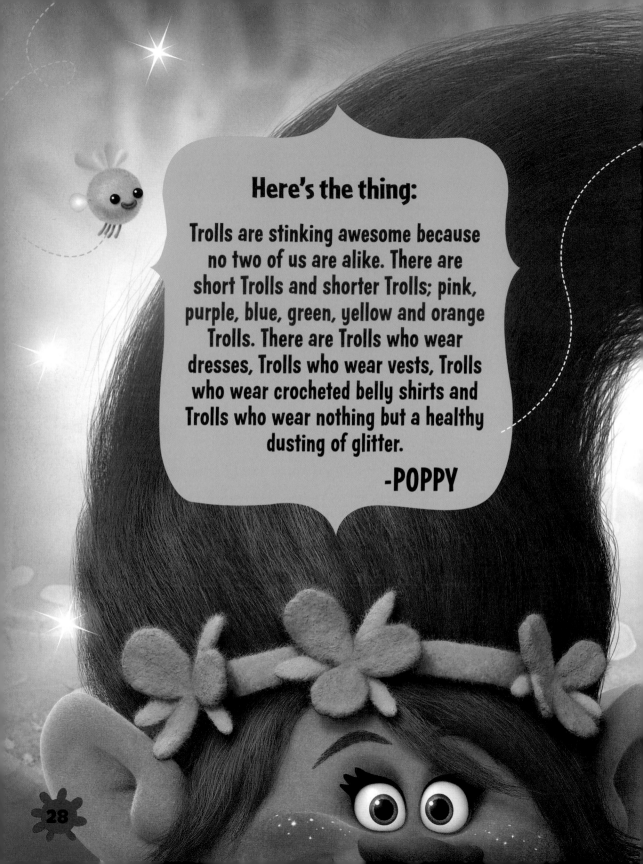

**Here's the thing:**

Trolls are stinking awesome because no two of us are alike. There are short Trolls and shorter Trolls; pink, purple, blue, green, yellow and orange Trolls. There are Trolls who wear dresses, Trolls who wear vests, Trolls who wear crocheted belly shirts and Trolls who wear nothing but a healthy dusting of glitter.

-POPPY

We also have a lot in common...

...almost all of us have bright shocks of hair...

...we all love to sing and dance...

...and we all love super-epic hug sessions!

# TROLL ANATOMY

Troll hair can be used for almost anything: expressing mood, camouflage or even as rope to swing through the trees!

Every Troll wears a watch made of Troll hair. It blossoms on the hour, every hour to announce Hug Time.

14.5cm

7.5cm

2.5cm

The average Troll grows to 7.5cm

Some Trolls only grow to 2.5cm!

Troll bodies are covered in a fuzzy texture similar to peach fuzz or a tennis ball. Some Trolls have sparkly glitter on their bodies, too.

Giant Trolls can grow to 14.5cm!

THESE ARE THE TROLLS' LIFE-SIZE HEIGHTS!

31

HEY DUDE!

HAIR WE GO!

# HA HA!

**What did the sticker say to the scrapbook?**

I'm stuck on you.

**What dance does Cooper do when decorating cupcakes?**

The sprinkler.

**Why did the Troll bring a ladder to school?**

He wanted a higher education.

36

# Trolls twin

Which Troll are you most like? Take the quiz and find out!

 **1**

**I am:**

a   an awesome advisor

b   someone with fashionable hair

c   totally groovy

d   artsy

e   outdoorsy

**2**

**My favourite thing to do is:**

a   state the obvious

b   get dressed up

c   dance, dance, dance!

d   bring out the true colours
    in everything I see

e   explore nature

**3**

My favourite outfit is:

a    loose shirts and baggy trousers

b    all of them

c    anything really colourful

d    something I made myself

e    something warm and cosy

**4**

My friends say I'm:

a    full of wisdom

b    outgoing

c    a little weird

d    creative

e    totally organic

**5**

If I went to Troll Village
I would...

a    meditate on everything groovy

b    get a Troll party started

c    make friends and find out
     where the next party is

d    pull out my sketchbook
     and start drawing

e    explore all the natural wonders
     and befriend all the creatures

Discover your Trolls twin on page 94.

# meet the TROLLS

# POPPY

This positively poptimistic Troll was singing before she could speak and dancing before she could crawl. It's no surprise that Poppy has been hosting rockin' parties since she was just one! Relentlessly upbeat, Poppy wields her positivity like a superpower, forever encouraging her friends to believe that with a song in your heart, anything is possible. This bubbly attitude has the ability to bring everyone together.

## FACTS ABOUT POPPY

**PERSONALITY:** eternally optimistic

**LIVES IN:** her own bright pink pod

**WORLD VIEWS:** everything sounds better with a cowbell!

**HOBBIES:** singing, dancing, hugging, partying and scrapbooking... to name a few

**CLOSE FRIENDSHIPS:** Poppy is friends with everyone! Whether they are a Troll, critter or even a Bergen

**BEST KNOWN FOR:** her upbeat attitude and love of scrapbooking

This friendly Troll is easily recognised by her bright shock of hair and trademark teal felt headband with cornflower blue flowers. If she's not out visiting her many friends she is most often found in her brightly coloured pod scrapbooking or handcrafting invitations to her next party. Poppy is well known for her scrapbook – which she takes everywhere safely tucked in her hair – and her love of bedazzling. After all, what doesn't look better with some stickers and glitter?

POPPY'S FIRST WORD WAS COWBELL!

# BRANCH

All the Trolls believe in the power of a hug, a song and a dance. All of them, except one: Branch. Certain that he is the only sane individual in a village of exuberantly happy Trolls, Branch tends to be reclusive and a little antisocial. Safe and content in his underground bunker (with provisions to last over ten years and even its own panic room) Branch is not your typical Troll.

## FACTS ABOUT BRANCH

**PERSONALITY:** determined and cautious

**LIVES IN:** an underground bunker

**HOBBIES:** preparing for the worst – a Bergen invasion

**CLOSE FRIENDSHIPS:** Poppy

**BEST KNOWN FOR:** shouting 'the Bergens are coming!' at inappropriate moments

It is Branch's practical and overly prepared nature however that keeps the Trolls safe when he and Poppy undertake their quest in Bergen Town. During their adventure Branch also learns the importance of friendship and finally allows himself to let his true colours shine. Known for being the Troll who cried 'Bergen', Branch struggles to tone down his overly cautious nature. With a little help from Poppy and their friends he's sure to get there one day!

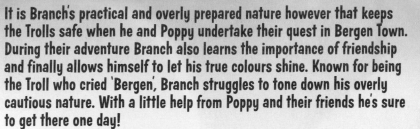

**BRANCH'S BUNKER**

**BRANCH HAS AN EXCEPTIONALLY BEAUTIFUL SINGING VOICE!**

# SATIN & CHENILLE

As the most fashion-forward members in Troll Village, Satin and Chenille are always on trend and have an extensive knowledge of fashion history. What they don't know about fashion is not worth knowing! These BFFF's (Best Fashion Friends Forever) are responsible for creating all of Poppy's pre-party, coronation and post-celebration outfits, and are always ready to lend a hand in getting Trolls ready for a party.

Though these twins are joined at the hair, this fashion duo is all about independence; they will never, ever, EVER wear the same outfit at the same time. They are also known for having multiple costume changes at every event. Fortunately, four hands make quick work!

Satin is the pink Troll and Chenille is the blue Troll.

# GUY DIAMOND

Blessed with oodles of confidence, this friendly, glittery Troll knows how to get any party started and can always be found at the centre, shining like a living disco ball. Guy Diamond's upbeat energy rubs off on all those around him, just like the glitter that covers him from head to toe. If you can't see him, just follow the trail of sparkly dust!

Who needs clothes when you have glitter?

# BIGGIE

Biggie's imposing stature is at extreme odds with his personality; this giant Troll is a huge softie! He is the biggest Troll in the village, with the biggest heart. When he's not bursting into happy tears, Biggie spends his time dressing up his pet worm, Mr Dinkles, for impromptu photo shoots. Biggie takes his pet everywhere with him, and has over one hundred photos of him!

Biggie is a big advocate for the short-vest-no-shirt look.

# COOPER

With double the feet of the average Troll, Cooper busts the craziest dance moves in all of Troll Village! Cooper is also the most enthusiastic Troll in the whole village. With his blue yarn-like hair, an extra-magical full coat of Troll hair and the special skill of pooping cupcakes, it's no wonder he's such a popular Troll to have around!

This charming Troll is renowned for his wicked harmonica solos!

# SMIDGE

Smidge is a tiny Troll with a surprisingly deep baritone voice. In addition to possessing super-strong hair, Smidge also has a super-strong body. This tiny Troll is also extremely disciplined when it comes to fitness and nutrition and loves turning any dance number into a quick workout. In her downtime Smidge likes to relax with a little death metal music or crochet work.

Snack Pack Member

This Troll will take any chance to show off her strength!

# DJ SUKI

As Troll Village's resident mash-up expert, DJ Suki can always be counted on to lay down some sweet beats, which regularly cause impromptu day-long dance parties. The secret to her unique sound? Her all-natural DJ equipment! This musical Troll jams with small critters to scratch and mix her music. With her ruby belly gem, yarn headphones and orange dreadlocks, this Troll knows how to stand out in a crowd!

DJ Suki loves to drop a needle-scratch in awkward moments.

# KING PEPPY

As the brave leader of the Trolls, King Peppy led his people to freedom and ushered in a new era of happiness and security for Troll Village. It is he who first uttered 'No Troll left behind', a mantra that later led his daughter Poppy to undertake a daring quest to rescue her friends. A little more forgetful now than he was as a young Troll, he regularly finds his misplaced items stuck within his hair.

King Peppy's heroism is the stuff of Troll legend!

# FUZZBERT

An enigma wrapped in a riddle, all anyone has ever seen of Fuzzbert is his green hair and two orange feet. Fuzzbert communicates not through words, but in guttural noises. He may not hear very well beneath those thick locks of hair but he certainly isn't lacking in personality! Fuzzbert loves to tickle other Trolls, and when he laughs, all of his hair shakes!

Fuzzbert's nickname is Twinkle Toes!

# HARPER

In Harper's eyes there is no such thing as a canvas too small or too large! With a pod full to the brim with artwork, it's no surprise that Harper also runs the Troll Village art studio and the Follow Your Art Gallery. A true artist, Harper never fails to listen when her paintings speak to her and she is always covered in paint of every colour imaginable from hair-to-toe, except, oddly enough, her smock!

Harper's eyes are unique. One of them is red and the other is green!

# CYBIL

Cybil shares her wisdom with anyone who will listen. Absorbed 'in the moment', Cybil sometimes forgets conversations from one minute ago, but hang around her long enough and you'll be coasting on a gentle wave of harmony. Don't forget, 'a door is just a barrier to the next room'.

When she's happy Cybil literally floats on air!

# MADDY

Maddy is known for working wonders with a Troll's already magical hair, styling and shaping it into amazing new creations. When she's not busy running the local hair salon in Troll Village, Maddy loves to team up with Satin and Chenille, pairing her trendy hairdos with their latest couture.

Maddy can take any Troll's hair to new heights of style!

# KARMA

Karma is happiest when she is frolicking in the forest. Her home is a greenhouse (although in Troll Village it's more of a rainbow house!). She is the village's best tunneller and climber. Not only is Karma an expert whittler and leaf-working specialist, but she can even mimic the calls of all the forest's many critters!

Karma loves the feel of Troll Village's enchanted soil between her toes!

# CREEK

Calm, collected and capable, Creek was always known for being a Troll's Troll – the guys all wanted to be him and the girls wanted to be around him. Creek was positive, supportive and reassuring (both as a friend and a dance partner), but he would somehow always manage to steal the spotlight and become the centre of attention.

Creek's freckles are made of glitter!

BFFF!
(best fashion
friends forever)

# HA HA!

How did
the Troll feel during her
gymnastic routine?

Head over heels.

Why did the sheet
music run away from
the singing Troll?

She kept hitting
all the notes.

Why did the
mushroom
like to party?

Because he was
a fungi!

Did you hear the one
about the fungus?

Just wait,
it'll grow on you.

Why did the fungi
leave Poppy's party?

There wasn't
mushroom.

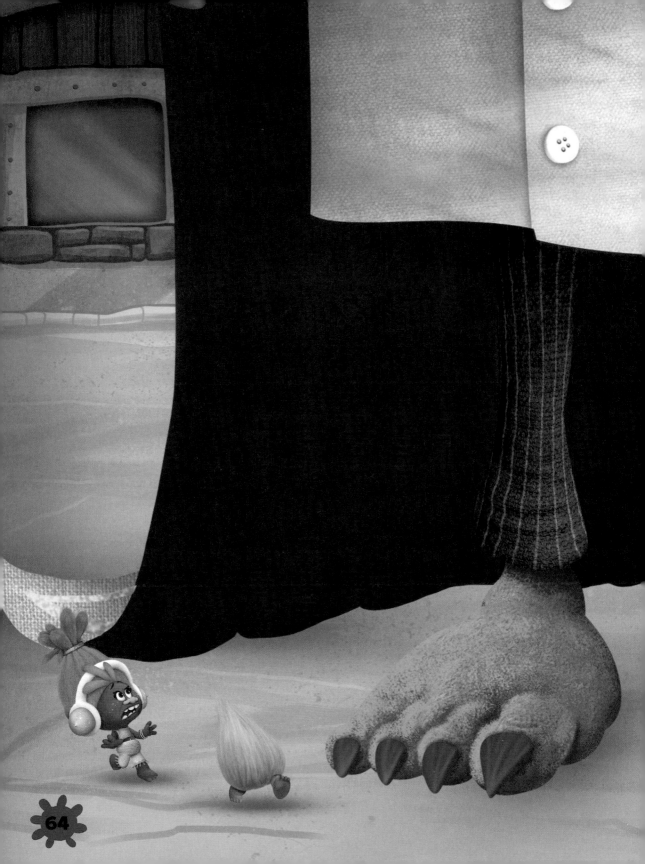

# A stroll through BERGEN TOWN

# BERGEN TOWN

A bustling metropolis of industry and convenience, Bergen Town is home to the crowded population of Bergens – large, lumbering creatures who think of themselves as fancy and sophisticated. After all, who else would extend their pinkie when drinking orange soda or wear a freshly pressed bib to every meal?

Strolling along the main street of Bergen Town there are a few places you simply must drop by...

## CAPTAIN STARFUNKLE'S ROLLER RINK AND ARCADE

In the eyes of King Gristle, there is no place fancier for a first date than the town's premier all-you-can-eat pizza buffet. With its deliciously greasy pizza, arcade games and roller rink, Captain Starfunkle's is the most fun place to visit in Bergen Town!

## BIBBLY BIBBINGTON'S BIBBERY

Do you have a fancy date planned? Or perhaps a Trollstice feast to attend? Either way you had better stop by Bibbly Bibbington's Bibbery for a new bib befitting the occasion. The proprietor, Bibbly, knows just how long a Bergen's bib should be (and how to flatter King Gristle into buying more than he needs). You may even get to see Bibbly's most prized possession – the vintage bib worn by King Gristle Senior at his first Trollstice!

# THE TROLL TREE

The Troll Tree is where the Bergens held the Trolls captive for many years. Every year at the Trollstice celebration, the Bergens would cook and eat some of the Trolls. It was the Bergens' one time of the year that they could experience happiness.

This is where the Trolls hung the fake wooden Poppy that King Gristle (then known as Prince Gristle) ate, at his first Trollstice.

King Peppy led the Trolls in their escape using these tunnels, guided by the light of the Torch of Freedom.

When the Trolls escaped, the Troll Tree fell into disrepair and eventually died.

According to Cloud Guy, one of these tunnels leads to certain DEATH... DEATH... DEATH.

These are the tunnels Poppy and Branch used to reach Bergen Town and save their friends.

# BERGEN TOWN CASTLE

Overlooking Bergen Town is King Gristle's castle. The Trolls never had time for a guided tour, but here's what they discovered on their adventure.

Before the Trolls arrived, the Banquet Hall was a very glum room. How could it not be with King Gristle Senior watching over it with a grim gaze?

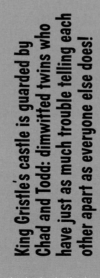

King Gristle's castle is guarded by Chad and Todd: dimwitted twins who have just as much trouble telling each other apart as everyone else does!

# BRIDGET

You will never find a sweeter or more kind-hearted Bergen in all of Bergen Town. When Poppy and her friends helped Bridget create the persona of Lady Glittersparkles, she discovered her courage and confidence. Not only did she stand up for her friends (and save them from being eaten), but she even caught the eye of her secret crush, King Gristle, and helped the entire Bergen kingdom to understand where happiness really comes from.

This couple bonded over a love of roller-skating.

72

# COUPLE

## KING GRISTLE

Mortified by his father's Trollstice blunder and desperate to win the love of his subjects, King Gristle Junior vowed to get Trolls back on the menu and return happiness to Bergen Town. He was right about one thing: the Trolls were certainly the key to happiness... just not in the way he expected!

Barnabus is King Gristle's faithful pet alligator. The only way to truly calm this guard-gator down is to play some slow jams.

73

# DISGRACED BERGENS

## CHEF

Chef had it all: a sterling reputation, throngs of admirers, a coveted spot in the Royal Kitchen and, most importantly, influence over the king. But all of that crumbled apart the day the Trolls escaped from the Troll Tree. Craving revenge with a side of Troll, Chef wandered the forest in exile for twenty years before she succeeded in recapturing the Trolls... and we all know how that turned out for her!

Chef knows many Troll recipes, including Troll-loaf and egg-Trolls.

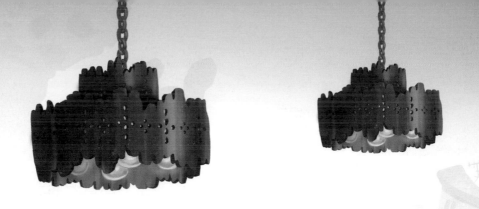

# KING GRISTLE SENIOR

This Bergen king was disgraced after the embarrassing incident at his son's first Trollstice celebration (the Trolls escaped!). The loss of the Trolls crushed the King. It led to him being dethroned and his son taking the crown early. He does have one impressive deed to his name though – he still holds the record for the most orange soda swallowed in one sitting... twenty-seven litres!

Even in retirement this Bergen was convinced that happiness could only be found in a tasty Troll treat.

# HA HA!

How does the Troll in the moon cut his hair?

E-clipse it!

How do you wrap a cloud?

With a rainbow.

What clothes do clouds wear?

Thunderwear.

What did the cloud say to the lightning bolt?

You're shocking!

# Let's play!

Cut out the Trolls tokens opposite and get ready to play some Troll-tastic games!

## MEMORY MUDDLE

Find a friend or family member to play this game with.

⭐ place all of your Trolls tokens onto a table and take a good look at them

⭐ player 1 looks away while player 2 takes one Trolls token away

⭐ player 1 then has to remember (and guess) which Trolls token is missing

⭐ then, it's player 2's turn to look away while player 1 removes a Trolls token

⭐ to make it harder you can remove more Trolls tokens each time. The player with the most correct guesses - wins!

Turn the page for more fun games to play...

82

# GUESS WHO

Find a friend or family member to play this game with.

- ⭐ place all your Trolls tokens onto a table
- ⭐ take it in turns to close your eyes, then point to a Trolls token
- ⭐ keep your eyes closed then ask questions, to try to work out which Trolls token you are pointing to
- ⭐ when you've guessed the right answer, it's the other player's turn

# HIDE AND SEEK

Find a friend or family member to play this game with.

- ⭐ player 1 looks away while player 2 hides the Trolls tokens around a room or garden
- ⭐ player 1 then has to find them. When all the Trolls tokens are found it's player 2's turn to hide and then find them
- ⭐ make it even more fun by giving a clue about the Trolls token hidden, when the seeker gets close to it

# Troll tale

Once upon a time, in a happy forest filled with happy trees, there lived the happiest creatures the world had ever known:

## the Trolls.

They loved to sing and dance and hug. A lot!

One day was an especially happy day in Troll Village. Poppy was going to throw a big party!

Everyone was excited to celebrate – except Branch. He didn't like singing, dancing or hugging. Instead, he spent his time worrying about the Bergens.

Long ago, the Bergens had captured Trolls and eaten them! The Bergens thought that eating Trolls brought them happiness. Luckily, many of the Trolls had escaped... until now.

Poppy's celebration was the biggest, loudest, craziest party ever! It was so loud that the Bergen Chef found where the Trolls had been living all these years. Most of the Trolls managed to hide. But Chef was able to scoop up several of them, including Poppy's closest friends, Satin and Chenille, Cooper, Biggie, Guy Diamond, Smidge, DJ Suki and Creek.

Continued on the next page...

# Troll tale

Chef couldn't wait to bring the tasty Trolls back to Bergen Town.

Poppy had to save her friends! She convinced Branch to help her. The sooner they could get to Bergen Town, the sooner they could rescue everybody and make it home safely!

Meanwhile, thanks to Chef, King Gristle would finally get to eat a Troll – and experience happiness! The king decided to have a big celebration called Trollstice so all the Bergens could eat Trolls and become happy, too.

When Poppy and Branch got to King Gristle's castle, they found most of their friends hidden in a cage in Bridget, the maid's, room.

But Creek was missing. Bridget agreed to help them find Creek if they could get King Gristle to notice her.

Poppy knew what to do. Satin and Chenille made Bridget a glitter jumpsuit. Then all the Trolls sat on her head to make

a SUPER-COLOURFUL RAINBOW WIG. Bridget loved her makeover. She called herself Lady Glittersparkles. The king would certainly notice her now!

When King Gristle saw Lady Glittersparkles, he fell in love. He didn't realize she was his maid. The king took her roller-skating. He showed her his new locket. Creek was inside it!

Continued on the next page...

87

# Troll tale

Later, the Trolls snuck into the king's room to save Creek. They grabbed the locket and zoomed past the king, his pet and his guards.

But when Poppy opened the locket, Creek wasn't there! Poppy was sad to learn that to save his own life, Creek had told Chef where all the other Trolls of Troll Village were hiding. How could Creek have betrayed his friends?

Then everyone was trapped in a pot! Poppy lost all hope and her colour started to fade. The other Trolls lost their colour, too – they turned grey with sadness.

Suddenly, they heard a beautiful voice singing. It was Branch! His singing brought out his true colours – he turned bright green with purple hair. He sang because his heart was full of the hope and joy that Poppy had showed him. He loved Poppy and Poppy loved Branch. She and the other Trolls started to sing, too, and their true colours came back.

Bridget couldn't let the Bergens eat her friends. She lifted the cover off the pot so the Trolls could escape.

At Trollstice, the Bergens, eager to finally get a taste of happiness, were angry to discover that Bridget had set the Trolls free.

Just then, the Trolls burst in to save her. They formed the rainbow wig again... and landed right on Bridget's head.

When King Gristle learned that Lady

88

Glittersparkles was actually Bridget, he was overjoyed. He realized that he didn't need to eat a Troll to be happy. All he needed was a full heart and Bridget by his side.

Branch told everyone how miserable he'd been until Poppy had taught him how to dance, hug and sing. Before long, all the Bergens were dancing and singing, too. The only Bergen who wasn't happy was Chef. Now that no one wanted to eat Trolls, she was out of a job! Chef and Creek were banished from Bergen Town, destined to be unhappy together. The Trolls had brought happiness to Bergen Town! The Bergens and the Trolls could now live in peaceful harmony.

# General Troll-edge

Put your Troll know-how to the test with this bumper TRUE or FALSE quiz.

|  | TRUE | FALSE |
|---|---|---|
| 1. Chef discovers where Trolls live after she hears Poppy's party. | ⭐ | ⭐ |
| 2. Chef is the ultimate party pooper and kidnaps Poppy and Branch. | ⭐ | ⭐ |
| 3. The Bergens believe eating Trolls will make them burp. | ⭐ | ⭐ |
| 4. DJ Suki uses small critters to help scratch and mix her tunes. | ⭐ | ⭐ |
| 5. Maddy is the best hairdresser in Troll Village. | ⭐ | ⭐ |
| 6. Fuzzbert's nickname is Furry Toes. | ⭐ | ⭐ |
| 7. King Gristle's pet alligator is called Barnabus. | ⭐ | ⭐ |

**TRUE    FALSE**

8. Biggie's pet is a worm.

**TRUE    FALSE**

9. King Gristle creates a special day called Trollstice for the Bergen to eat Trolls.

**TRUE    FALSE**

10. King Gristle keeps Creek inside his roller-skate, until Creek escapes.

**TRUE    FALSE**

11. When Branch sings, he turns his true colour of bright pink.

**TRUE    FALSE**

12. The Trolls form a rainbow wig to help Bridget transform into Lady Glittersparkles.

**TRUE    FALSE**

13. Chef is banished with Cooper and Smidge after the Trolls make everyone happy.

**TRUE    FALSE**

14. The Trolls bring lots of happiness to Bergen Town.

Find the answers on page 94.

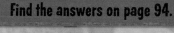

**93**

# ANSWERS

**Page 38**
If you answered...
mostly a's - you are Creek
mostly b's - you are Poppy
mostly c's - you are Cooper
mostly d's - you are Harper
mostly e's - you are Karma

**Page 92**
1-TRUE
2-TRUE
3-FALSE
4-TRUE
5-TRUE
6-FALSE

7-TRUE
8-TRUE
9-TRUE
10-FALSE
11-FALSE
12-TRUE
13-FALSE
14-TRUE